SNOOPY

features as

The Flying Ace

Charles M. Schulz

Printed and bound in Great Britain
for Ravette Publishing Limited,
Unit 3, Tristar Centre,
Star Road, Partridge Green,
West Sussex RH13 8RA
by Cox & Wyman, Berkshire.

ISBN: 1 84161 027 5

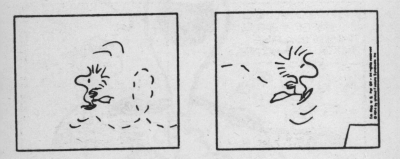

HERE'S THE WORLD WAR I FLYING ACE WALKING ALONG A COUNTRY ROAD IN FRANCE...

HE NOTICES A BEAUTIFUL YOUNG GIRL APPROACHING FROM THE OPPOSITE DIRECTION...HE SPEAKS..

2-1

BONJOUR, SWEETIE!

SHE IS NOT IMPRESSED BY HIS FLUENT FRENCH

© 1979 United Feature Syndicate, Inc.

SCHULZ

HERE'S THE WORLD WAR I FLYING ACE SOARING OVER THE FRONT LINES IN HIS SOPWITH CAMEL...

2-3

HE WAVES TO THE POOR BLIGHTERS IN THE TRENCHES BELOW

IN THEIR ADMIRATION FOR HIM THEY SHOWER HIM WITH GIFTS...

LIKE ROCKS!

SCHULZ

© 1979 United Feature Syndicate, Inc.   2-10

8-12

STAY RIGHT WHERE YOU ARE, OR I'LL POUND YOU!

THIS IS GOING TO BE HARD TO DO...

3-16

© 1984 United Feature Syndicate, Inc.

YES, MA'AM..UNDER HERE, I'M HERE!

BONK!

SCHULZ

Other PEANUTS™ titles published by Ravette ...

Snoopy Features as ...

The Literary Ace	1 84161 026 7	£2.99
The Matchmaker	1 84161 028 3	£2.99
The Fitness Fanatic	1 84161 029 1	£2.99

Snoopy Laughter and Learning series
wipe clean pages
(a fun series of story and activity books for preschool
and infant school children)

available July 2000

Read with Snoopy	1 84161 016 X	£2.50
Write with Snoopy	1 84161 017 8	£2.50
Count with Snoopy	1 84161 018 6	£2.50
Colour with Snoopy	1 84161 019 4	£2.50

PEANUTS™ Anniversary Treasury
(224 pages featuring some of Charlie Brown's favourite
strips in colour and black & white)

available August 2000	1 84161 021 6	£9.99

You Really Don't Look 50, Charlie Brown
(over 500 daily and Sunday strips and a series of
Charles Schulz essays celebrating this anniversary
year).

available Sept 2000	1 84161 020 8	£6.99

Prices are subject to change without prior notice.

All PEANUTS™ books are available from your local bookshop or from the address below. Just tick the titles required and send the form with your payment to:-

BBCS, P.O. Box 941, Kingston upon Hull HU1 3YQ
24-hr telephone credit card line 01482 224626

Prices and availability are subject to change without prior notice.

Please enclose a cheque or postal order made payable to BBCS to the value of the cover price of the book and allow the following for postage and packing:-

UK & BFPO:	£1.95 (weight up to 1kg)	3-day delivery
	£2.95 (weight over 1kg up to 20kg)	3-day delivery
	£4.95 (weight up to 20kg)	next day delivery

| EU & Eire: | Surface Mail: | £2.50 for first book & £1.50 for subsequent books |
| | Airmail: | £4.00 for first book & £2.50 for subsequent books |

| USA: | Surface Mail: | £4.50 for first book & £2.50 for subsequent books |
| | Airmail: | £7.50 for first book & £3.50 for subsequent books |

| Rest of the World: | Surface Mail: | £6.00 for first book & £3.50 for subsequent books |
| | Airmail: | £10.00 for first book & £4.50 for subsequent books |

Name: ....

Address: ....

....

....

Cards accepted: Visa, Mastercard, Switch, Delta, American Express

Expiry date .... Signature ....